Sticker Fun ACTIVITY BOOK

SANTA'S BUSY NIGHT

Have fun completing the sticker and doodling activities! Look at the sticker sheets. Can you find a sticker that fits? When you are sure you have found the right sticker, carefully peel it off and stick it down. There are also cute press-outs and extra stickers to use anywhere you want!

make believe ideas

Christmas delivery

ELF EXPRESS

Use stickers to load the van, then colour it.

Write your name on the letter and sticker the stamp!

Colour the elf and sticker his new shoes.

In a tangle!

Follow the lines to find out which button turns on the Christmas lights.

Get to the North Pole!

Help the penguin through the maze to reach the North Pole.

Start

Finish

Colour the penguins.

Letter to Santa

Find the missing stickers. Then, colour the toys on the Christmas list.

1.

2.

3.

Pretty patterns

Use colour to finish the patterns.

Perfect presents

Colour the fairy and the presents.

Find the matching presents.

Beautiful baubles

Colour and sticker the decorations.

Colour **Santa's** comfy **bed!**

Find the missing stickers to see what's under the bed.

Christmas car

Follow the lines to see which elf will drive the car.

Draw faces on the elves.

Sticker presents in the car.

The night before Christmas

Colour the town.

Circle three elves.

13

Colour the clothes for **Mrs Claus.**

Circle five mice.

Winter woollens

Find the matching hats.

Circle four differences between the penguins.

Style the sleigh!

Copy Santa. Use the grid to help you.

Find the missing stickers.

Colour Santa's sleigh.

Cute cards

Press out and complete the Christmas cards,
and then give them to friends or family.

Pages 2-3

Page 6

Pages 8-9

Pages 10-11

Page 15

Page 16

Extra stickers